I dedicate this little fable to my grandchildren
Jasper and Robin, my great nephew Magnus and
my great niece Paloma.

HARE & HERON PRESS

Published by Hare & Heron Press 2015
14 Court Road, Lewes, East Sussex BN7 2SA
www.hareandheronpress.com

Written by Julian Warrender
Illustrated by Lyndsey Smith
Designed and produced by Carlotta Luke
Edited by Dorothy Stannard
Hare & Heron Press logo designed and drawn by James Otway
Printed by East Communications
using vegetable-based ink on FSC accredited paper

FSC
MIX
Paper from
responsible sources
FSC® C018405

Magnus Carter was a hard-working, brave little mole. He had a stubby tail, a twitchy pink nose fringed with whiskers, and velvety, chocolate-brown fur. He had a strong, stocky body and used his large paddle-shaped front paws to dig, shovel and push earth to make the maze of tunnels leading to King Moldewarp's palace.

Every day Magnus and his friends collected plump, pink, wriggly worms to feed the royal household. While the greedy King grew fat, poor Magnus's tummy rumbled, his pups mewed with hunger, and his wife was sad and silent. On some days, no one smiled, even when Magnus sang their favourite song.

agnus and his family lived deep underground in a tiny, cramped burrow. They never saw daylight, or smelt the sweet scent of flowers, or heard the trilling and tweeting of birdsong. They could not gaze at the star-sprinkled night sky or dance by the light of the harvest moon. Life was unfair.

Above ground there was a beautiful meadow covered in "molehills". Only King Moldewarp and his family were allowed to have fun building these humps of crumbling earth. In winter, when snow was on the ground, the King and Queen liked to sledge down the hillocks; in summer, they played croquet on the flat grassy areas.

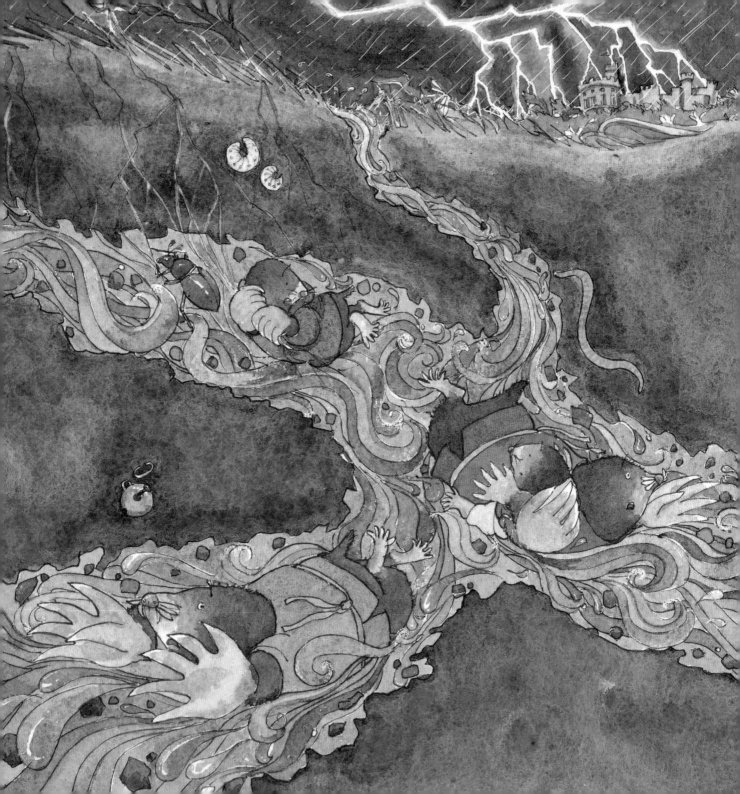

Then, one night, in the winter of 1214, there was a great storm. It rained without a break for five grim days and five wild nights. Water poured through the tunnels, sweeping the mole families away. "Help!" cried the pups, as they clung to the roots of a tree. Many moles drowned trying to reach the surface, while King Moldewarp and his family remained safe and dry.

The moles were very sad to see such destruction but the King was heartless. "Now the storm is over, you moles must repair the damage, and only then will you get paid," bellowed the King. "Bring me worms, more worms – NOW!"

Later that evening the moles got together. "Let's draw up a petition," said Magnus. "We shall tell the King that we will do no more digging until he agrees to our rights – to play above ground, make molehills, feed our families and live in peace."

Molehills for all moles

A brave group of moles led by Magnus went to see King Moldewarp, who was very angry. "You are a troublemaker, Magnus Carter," screeched the King. "Throw him in jail!" he ordered the guards.

In the bleak, uncomfortable dungeon, poor Magnus felt lonely and frightened. He was worried about his family. The other moles challenged the King. "We won't dig for worms until you free Magnus and listen to us. We shall block up the tunnels," said the bold band of friends.

A t first, the King was grumpy and cross, but he was also getting hungry. The moles had raided the palace kitchens and locked the larder door; things were getting serious. "I give in, you are free to go," said King Moldewarp. On the day Magnus left prison his friends danced with joy and praised his courage.

Dungeon

Later that year, on 15th June, 1215, a grand ceremony was held. King Moldewarp promised all moles equal rights, with the freedom to dig for worms and build their own molehills. He sealed an important looking scroll that became known as Magnus Carter's Charter. Everyone cheered and shook paws; some moles shed tears of happiness.

To this day, fields and meadows are dotted with hundreds of hillocks and humps, and moles grow plump and contented on worms. With luck, on warm summer evenings, you may even see a few of them playing croquet!

King John ...the facts

✠ King John was a cruel, greedy and jealous man.

✠ He was born on December 24th, 1167.

✠ He became King of England in 1199.

✠ John quarrelled with his family, and went to war with France.

✠ He lost lots of land and had to raise taxes in England to pay for his defeats.

✠ King John became very unpopular and was given the nickname "John Softsword".

✠ In 1207 King John had another quarrel, this time with the Pope who was Head of the Church.

✠ The Pope said John was no longer King of England or a member of the Church.

✠ John's third and worst quarrel was with the people of England.

✠ By May 1215 a group of powerful barons, fed up with paying extra taxes, captured London.

✠ The rebels refused to give back London until King John agreed to their demands.

✠ In June 1215 King John met with his people at Runnymede, a meadow near the royal palace at Windsor, to agree and seal Magna Carta.

✠ On 15th June, 1215 Magna Carta was agreed and sealed.